DONNIE

CONTENTS

MEET LEONARDO...8

MEET MICHELANGELO.......................................10

MEET DONATELLO..12

MEET RAPHAEL...14

COMIC STORY: CHASING SHADOWS...................16

MEET SPLINTER...22

MEET APRIL..24

MUTAGEN MADNESS..26

AWESOME SKATEBOARD..................................28

DIMENSION X..29

MUTANT EXPLOSION..30

MEET THE VILLAINS...32

READY FOR ATTACK!.......................................36

MEET CASEY JONES...37

MEAN STREETS CHALLENGE............................38

EVIL SEARCH!...40

LEO COPY..41

DONNIE'S TOP INVENTIONS............................42

WHICH TURTLE IS MOST LIKE YOU?................44

COMIC STRIP..46

2014 - THE LOWDOWN....................................48

SPEED CONTROL..49

COMIC STORY: TAKEN......................................50

OOZE ATTACK..56

EVIL CREATION..57

RELEASE THE NINJA BOMBS!..........................58

GUIDE TO BEING AN AWESOME NINJA!...........60

SMASH!...62

ANSWERS...64

GOODBYE...66

POSTERS..67

The Turtles are back and they are ready to hit the streets of NYC!
With tons of new grossed-out mutants threatening their city —
and their family — these hard-fighting, fun-loving brothers
will stop at nothing in their quest for peace.

LOOKS LIKE

WE'VE GOT A MISSION

So ... are you ready
for a shellraiser of a ride?

IT'S GO TIME!

EGMONT
We bring stories to life

First published in Great Britain in 2014 by Egmont UK Limited
The Yellow Building, 1 Nicholas Road, London W11 4AN

© 2014 Viacom Overseas Holdings C.V. All Rights Reserved.
TEENAGE MUTANT NINJA TURTLES and all related titles, logos and characters
are trademarks of Viacom Overseas Holdings C.V.
Based on characters created by Peter Laird and Kevin Eastman.

Written by Laura Green. Designed by Ant Duke.

ISBN: 978 1 4052 7214 8
57521/2

Printed in Italy

MEET LEONARDO

Leo is one dedicated ninja! He spends all his spare time practising his fighting skills and takes his responsibility as leader very seriously. This sometimes annoys his brothers, but they know Leo would do anything to protect them. With new mutants on the scene, Leo is even more ready to go hero!

Leo says ...
"HEROES DON'T ASK FOR PERMISSION!"

Fast Facts!

Species: human/turtle mutant
Lives: in the sewers of New York City
Personality: brave, dedicated, loyal, confident
Weapon: the katana – a Japanese sword
Guilty pleasure: a sci-fi show called 'Space Heroes'!

DONOTCHORACE! Awesome ninjas must learn to observe a situation carefully before an attack! Take this observation test to see if you've got what it takes.

Which two pictures are exactly the same? Sounds easy? Well, set a clock ... you have 60 seconds to do it!

MEET MICHELANGELO

Mikey says ...
"HOT NUNCHUCK FURY!"

Mikey might be a goofball but he's a master of the nunchucks! He can trap the enemy with one nunchuck swing. When he's not playing pranks and doing skateboard tricks, Mikey shows promise of being a top-class warrior. Epic!

Did you know?

Mikey can hold his breath underwater for fifteen minutes!

FAST FACTS!

SPECIES: human/turtle mutant
LIVES: in the sewers of New York City
PERSONALITY: funny, creative, sociable, enthusiastic
WEAPON: nunchucks
GUILTY PLEASURE: cheese pizza!

BOMB OUT! Check out Mikey playing tricks on his brothers!
Can you spot 5 differences between the pictures?

Answers on page 64.

MEET DONATELLO

Donnie is the brains of the family. He is brilliant at inventing the coolest gadgets, vehicles and weapons to keep his brothers safe. Oh, and he's a master with his treasured weapon - the bo staff, too. Donnie is one mind-blowing ninja!

Donnie says ...
"THIS IS GONNA BE EPIC!"

DID YOU KNOW?

Donnie created a new mutant - Mutagen Man. And now it has a life of its own!

FAST FACTS!
Species: human/turtle mutant
Lives: in the sewers of New York City
Personality: clever, inventive, strategic, sensitive
Weapon: a six-foot bo staff
Slushy fact: he has a bit of a crush on April O'Neil!

AWESOME MACHINES!
Donatello invented the Turtle Sub – a special vehicle that can go underwater so the Turtles can spy on the underwater Kraang base.

Now it's your turn to invent an awesome machine! It needs to be able to speed through snow and ice. Design your vehicle below, label the parts and give it a name.

MEET RAPHAEL

DID YOU KNOW?

Raph is super bitter that Leo was chosen as leader over him!

Raph is one mean, green, ninja machine! He loves nothing more than being in an all-out battle. There's no hanging around for this Turtle - Raph is always in the middle of the action! He is fiercely loyal too - and will do ANYTHING to protect his family.

Raph says ...
"I WON. YOU LOST."

FAST FACTS!

SPECIES: human/turtle mutant

LIVES: in the sewers of New York City

PERSONALITY: strong, brave, hot-headed, rash

WEAPON: sai - two bladed prongs

SECRET: he tells his secrets to his pet tortoise, Spike

RAPH ATTACKS!

Uh oh. Raph is on the rampage and has punched a hole through these photographs! Can you work out who is in each picture?

Answers on page 64.

CHASING SHADOWS

SCRIPT: LANDRY WALKER & ED CARUANA, PENCILS: RYAN J NEAL,
COLOURS: JASON CARDY, LETTERS: ALEX FOOT.

MEET SPLINTER

splinter and shredder – the backstory!

Splinter once had a human life. His name was Hamato Yoshi and he lived in Japan with his wife, Tang Shen. A rival ninja named Oroku Saki killed her out of jealousy! Hamato was forced to flee to America. Oroku Saki now goes by the name of Shredder!

Splinter is a father figure to the Turtles. He is dedicated in training his sons in the ancient art of ninjutsu. Now he just has to work out how to get them to stick to the rules on the mean streets of NYC!

Fast Facts!

Mutant name: Splinter
Pre-mutant name: Hamato Yoshi
Lives: in the sewers underneath NYC
Role: ninjutsu master, father and sensei
Strengths: calm, wise, strong, strict
Enemy: Shredder

copy splinter

Use the grid to copy this picture of Splinter,
square by square.

MEET APRIL

When April met the Turtles, her life changed forever. Between pretending to be a regular kid at high school and helping the Turtles fight for peace, April trains with Splinter to become a female ninja – a kunoichi.

April says ...
"THINK NINJA!"

Did you know?

The Turtles mutated April's dad into a mutant bat – uh oh! She wasn't too happy with her shell-raising friends!

Fact File!

Species: human

Personality: clever, funny, brave, loyal

Strengths: she's an awesome spy!

Secret: April is made up of part Kraang DNA – she is half human, half mutant! Sssh!

Hidden Message

April has tapped into the Footbots' computer and she has found a coded message. Can you fill in the missing words so she can warn the Turtles?

We will wait for the Turtles opposite _____ _____ Restaurant. We know they will be there at _____. They can't resist _____. The Turtles cannot escape the mighty _____ any longer. Nobody must learn of this _____ to assassinate the Turtles. It is a _____ mission. Message over.

top-secret

5 o'clock

Antonio's Pizza

Shredder

cheese pizza

plot

challenge
April can spy danger anywhere. But can you spy the hidden Kraangdroid on these pages?

25

Answers on page 64.

MUTAGEN MADNESS!

The Turtles have made a big mistake. They've dropped a huge batch of mutagen onto the streets of NYC and now the city is at risk of mass mutation! Which ninja will recover the most mutagen canisters and keep the city safe?

START

CHALLENGE! SAY 10 WORDS ABOUT LEO AND PICK UP 3 CANISTERS.

3

Keep a note of how many canisters you pick up here.

4

7

6

YOU RESCUE 5 MUTAGEN CANISTERS FROM THE KRAANG'S WAREHOUSE. AWESOME!

YOU FIND 2 MUTAGEN CANISTERS!

You will need: a die and counters for up to four players.
How to play: decide which Turtle each player will be, then place your counter on the start. Take turns to roll the die and move through the city. There are tons of challenges to take and canisters to collect. Make a note of how many canisters you win in the Turtle boxes.
The first player with the most canisters when they get to the end, wins!

9

10

CHALLENGE! WHAT WEAPON DOES MIKEY USE? WIN 2 CANISTERS.

12

YOU STEAL 3 MUTAGEN CANISTERS FROM THE FOOTBOTS!

14

33 34

TIGER CLAW STEALS 2 OF YOUR MUTAGEN CANISTERS!

36

FINISH

FISHFACE STEALS 1 OF YOUR CANISTERS! MISS A GO.

31 23

CHALLENGE! NAME 2 OF DONNIE'S INVENTIONS. WIN 2 MUTAGEN CANISTERS!

YOU STOP MUTAGEN FROM MUTATING A GROUP OF CHILDREN! WIN 2 CANISTERS.

24

21

29

YOU STEAL 3 MUTAGEN CANISTERS FROM MUTAGAN MAN!

20

YOU DROP SOME MUTAGEN IN THE SUBWAY. LOSE 1 CANISTER.

CHALLENGE! STAND ON ONE FOOT FOR 2 MINUTES, WIN 3 MUTAGEN CANISTERS!

27 26

15 17 18

YOU SPOT 1 MUTAGEN CANISTER BEHIND A TRASH CAN.

AWESOME SKATEBOARD!

Mikey loves doing crazy stunts on his skateboard – from kickflips to noseslides, Mikey has got them all down! Design your own skateboard below.

DIMENSION X

The Turtles are trapped in the Kraang's home world – Dimension X. This place is seriously bizarre! But Mikey thinks he has worked out an escape plan. Guide Mikey through the maze to the portal back to Earth!

Portal to Earth!

Answers on page 64.

29

MUTANT EXPLOSION

Answers on page 64.

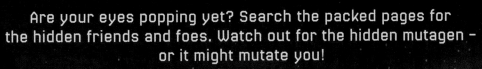

Are your eyes popping yet? Search the packed pages for the hidden friends and foes. Watch out for the hidden mutagen – or it might mutate you!

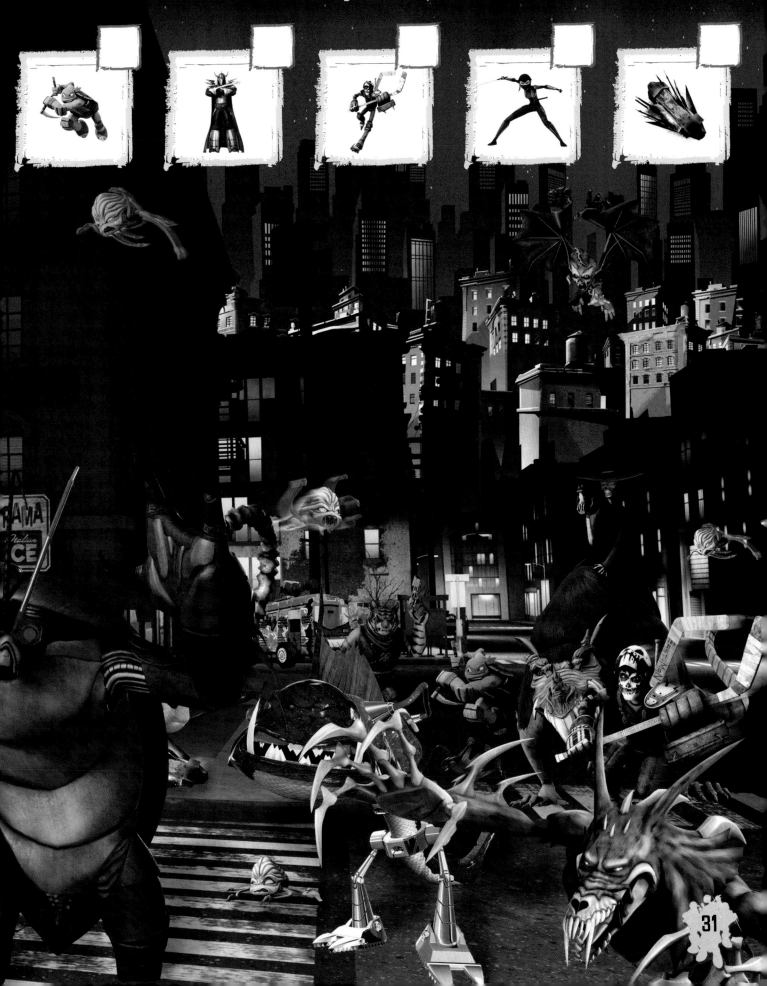

MEET THE VILLAINS

SHREDDER

Shredder is one dangerous enemy to have. From his long sharp claws to his deadly shoulder blades, he's built to destroy. He wants to wipe out the Turtles and he won't stop until he succeeds.

This dude is 100% evil!

Shredder Facts!

Name: Shredder

Place of Birth: Japan

Name in Japan: Oroku Saki

Role: evil crime lord in charge of the Footclan and the Footbots

The Footbots

This all-new robotic army are Shredder's top mutant foot soldiers.
They are super deadly – they can clone new moves in seconds!

Footbots Facts!

Leader: Shredder

Uniform: black so they can hide in the shadows

Species: robot/human mutant

Threat: they will stop at nothing to obey their master

Kraang Prime

The leader of the Kraang. He once trapped April so he could steal her energy to take over the world. The Turtles came to the rescue but his next plot is sure to be around the corner ...

Kraang Prime Facts!

size: a big dude - over 10 feet in diameter!

kraangdroid height: over 25 feet!

strength: he is stronger than any other Kraangdroid in the universe!

most likely to say ...
"ALL OF YOU WILL DIE HERE!"

Did you know?

The Kraang want to capture April so they can steal her DNA. April's DNA can perfect the Kraang's mutagen!

The Kraang

A race of pink, brain-like aliens from Dimension X. They brought mutagen to Earth!

MORE VILLAINS AND MUTANTS!

Karai

Karai is the adopted daughter of Shredder. Shredder raised her to become one of the toughest female ninjas in Japan. But she's had enough of being in Shredder's shadow. She's ready to break out on her own!

DID YOU KNOW?

Karai is Splinter's real daughter! Shredder took her when she was a baby.

Karai Facts!

Species: human

Role: an outlaw ninja assassin

Strengths: confident, strong, independent

tiger claw

Tiger Claw Facts!

Species: human/tiger mutant

Role: bounty hunter

Appearance: orange and black with sharp claws and teeth!

This villain mutated as a young boy in Japan and grew up as a circus performer before becoming Shredder's most deadly assassin. He is always ready for a fight!

A collision with some mutagen transformed Raph's pet tortoise, Spike, into a mutant on the rampage. He still loves Raph but he's determined to destroy the other Turtles – for good!

slash

slash Facts!

species: mutant tortoise

pre-mutant name: Spike

appearance: blue with yellow horns and a spiky shell!

Mutagen Man

A human fan of the Turtles who transformed into something much more dangerous when he had a run-in with some mutagen!

did you know?

Donnie used Mutagen Man to try and discover a cure to mutagen – but now he is way out of control!

Mutagen Man Facts!

species: human mutant

pre-mutant name: Timothy

appearance: a mess of guts, organs and slime!

READY FOR ATTACK!

Leonardo is ready to throw his ninja stars to show the Kraang who's boss! Can you help?

How to play: Take a close look at the page and try to remember where the Kraang are.

Close your eyes and then dot a pencil on the page where you think there is a Kraang.

You have 12 shots to hit them all! Don't hit the Turtles - they're on your side!

MEET CASEY JONES

Casey can be a hot-headed warrior but he is a great friend to April and the Turtles. He is especially close to Raph – they are both fiery souls!

April tutored Casey at school and now he will do anything to protect her. He is a useful guy to have around when things turn nasty!

Casey says ...
"GOONGALA!"

FAST FACTS!

SPECIES: human

LIVES: Brooklyn, NY

PERSONALITY: strong, brave, loyal, funny

WEAPON: sports gear

DID YOU KNOW?

Casey's nickname for April is 'Red'!

CASEY LOVES BEATING FRIENDS AT AN EPIC GAME OF HOCKEY. DESIGN YOUR VERY OWN HOCKEY STICK HERE!

37

MEAN STREETS CHALLENGE

The chase is on in NYC! The Turtles need to catch Mutagen Man
before he gets to April. It's go time!

There are eight differences between these two pictures. Design a shell
each time you find a difference.

Answers on page 64.

EVIL SEARCH!

Time to think, you shell brain! Find all of the evil names below in the grid and when you're finished, discover a hidden message from Shredder.

Write down all the letters in the green boxes and all the letters in the red boxes. Can you unscramble the letters to make two deadly words from Shredder?

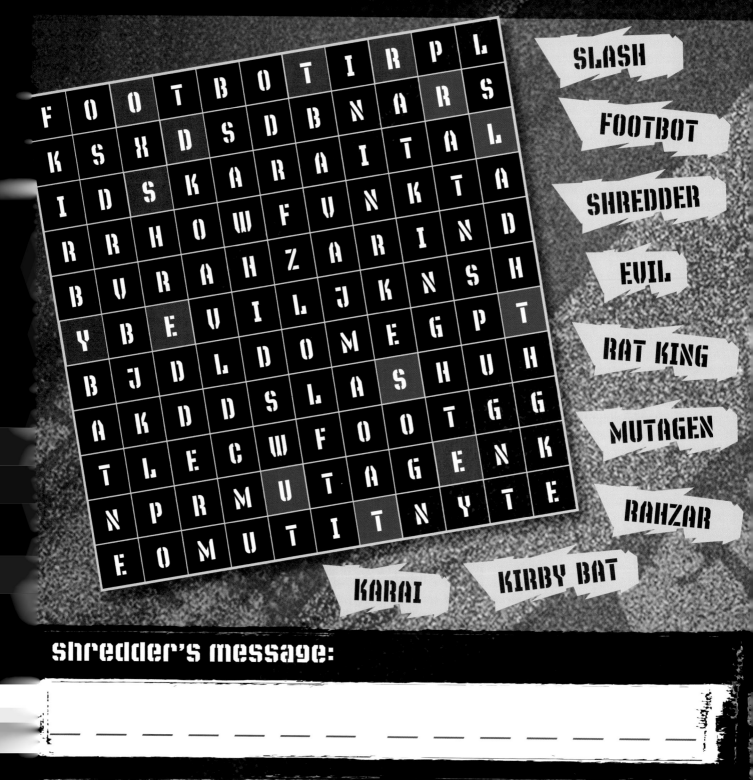

SLASH

FOOTBOT

SHREDDER

EVIL

RAT KING

MUTAGEN

RAHZAR

KARAI

KIRBY BAT

Shredder's message:

Answers on page 65.

LEO COPY

Do you want to bring Leo to life on the page? You do? Awesome! Copy this picture into the grid below.

DONNIE'S TOP INVENTIONS

Donnie has invented tons of weapons, gadgets and machines to keep the Turtles ahead of the game. Some inventions work better than others. Come and take a look around Donnie's wall of fame to see which ones fly and which ones sink ...

Give each invention a score out of 10 for awesome-ness!
Which one is your winner?

METALHEAD

A remote-controlled robot

History:
Created using the tech from a Kranngdroid body

Strengths:
Strong and powerful

Weakness:
Slow and heavy and the Kraang can control him too!

Fast Fact:
When he's under Donnie's control, his eyes are blue. When the Kraang take him over, his eyes are pink

T-PHONES

A special mobile phone

History:
Created so the Turtles can stay in contact on the streets of NYC

Strengths:
Super clever - they can hack into government satellites!

Weakness:
None - they are awesome!

Fast Fact:
If a bad guy steals the phone, they self-destruct!

THE SHELLRAISER

An awesome turtle-mobile!

retractable canon for shooting the bad guys

History:
Made from an old subway car, now it's a powerful machine!

Strengths:
Packed with kick-ass weapons and it can reach speeds of up to 123mph!

Weakness:
It can be noisy so is no good if the Turtles need to stay in the shadows

Fast Fact:
There is a stealth bike hidden inside for a quick escape

razor-toothed crusher on the front bumper

SPY-ROACH

A spying cockroach mutant!

History:
Donnie's pet roach, before it was turned into a mutant. The camera on his back spied on the bad guys

Strengths:
Super strong and can see through walls!

Weakness:
Impatient

Fast Fact:
Now he's been turned into a mutant, he wants to destroy Raph! This is one invention that's gone wrong!

STEALTH BIKE

An awesome motorbike with special powers

History:
Donnie built this shell-covered bike so the Turtles could make quick getaways

Strengths:
Its shell shield protects the rider from attack

Weakness:
There's only one - so the Turtles fight over it sometimes!

Fast Fact:
The shield is the same colour as the road so it has the ultimate camouflage!

43

WHICH TURTLE IS MOST LIKE YOU?

1.

A GROUP OF FOOTBOTS ARE WAITING FOR YOU OUTSIDE THE SEWERS. WHAT DO YOU DO?

A) CHARGE AT THEM – IT'S BATTLE TIME!

B) THROW A CHEESE PIZZA AT THEM TO DISTRACT THEM

C) TAKE FIVE MINUTES TO HATCH A CUNNING PLAN

D) USE YOUR NEW INVENTION – NINJA SMOKE BOMBS – TO CLOUD THEIR VISION

2.

WHAT DO YOU LIKE TO DO IN YOUR SPARE TIME?

A) TALK TO YOUR PETS

B) THROW WATER BOMBS AT YOUR FRIENDS

C) READ UP ON THE SECRETS OF NINJUTSU TRAINING

D) INVENT AWESOME MACHINES AND GADGETS!

3.

WHICH MOVIE WOULD YOU GO AND SEE AT THE CINEMA?

A) BATTLE TIME! THE ULTIMATE COMBAT ADVENTURE

B) MONKEY AROUND! THE FUNNIEST PRANKS FROM AROUND THE WORLD!

C) SPACE HEROES – THE MOVIE!

D) THE HISTORY OF METALLURGY – AN INVENTOR'S PARADISE

CE HEROES
HE MOVIE

4.
TIGER CLAW IS COMING TO GET YOU! WHAT DO YOU SHOUT?

A) "LET'S BASH SOME BOTS!"

B) "HOT NUNCHUCK FURY!"

C) "I HAVE A BOLD AND DARING PLAN."

D) "TIME TO UNLEASH MY NEW WEAPON – THE STUN GUN!"

5.
WHAT IS YOUR FAVOURITE THING ABOUT NYC?

A) THE BATTLES WITH BAD GUYS!

B) PARTIES AND PIZZA!

C) IT'S EASY TO STAY IN THE SHADOWS AND OBSERVE

D) THE AWESOME COMPUTER SHOPS!

SO WHO ARE YOU MOST LIKE?

MOSTLY As
RAPH!
YOU'RE BRAVE, TOUGH AND LOVE BEING IN THE MIDDLE OF THE ACTION!

MOSTLY Bs
MIKEY!
YOU'RE WILD AND FUN! YOU LOVE PLAYING PRANKS ON YOUR FRIENDS AND FINDING ADVENTURES.

MOSTLY Cs
LEO!
YOU ARE A TRUE LEADER AND LOVE MAKING AWESOME PLANS. YOU'RE A BORN NINJA WARRIOR!

MOSTLY Ds
DONNIE!
YOU ARE A SUPER-BRAIN AND LOVE ANYTHING TECHY. YOU'RE A ONE-STOP INVENTING MACHINE!

45

COMIC STRIP

Have you ever made up your own Turtle adventure? This is your chance to send your favourite Turtles on an awesome mission! These pages have been designed especially for you to make a comic strip. Fire up your imagination!

IT WAS A QUIET NIGHT ON THE STREETS OF NYC, UNTIL ...

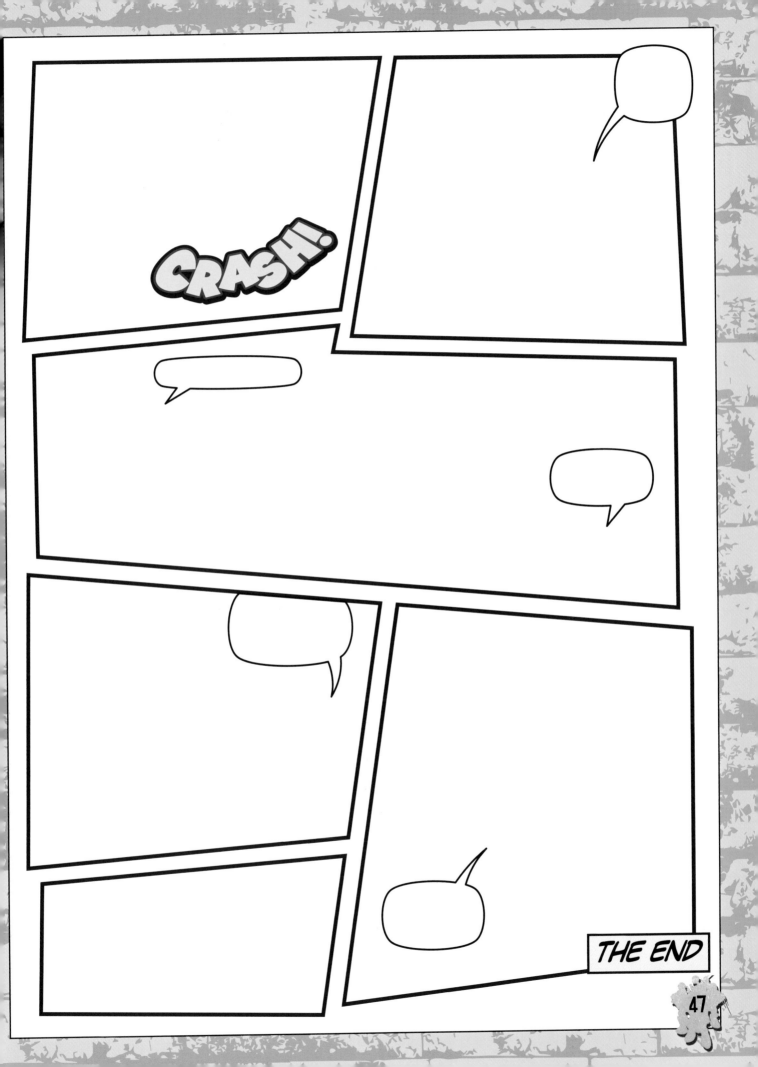

2014 – THE LOWDOWN!

Splinter asked the Turtles to keep a diary of all the things that went right and wrong for them in 2014. A good ninja will learn from their bomb-outs as well as their successes. Now it's your turn to do a round-up of your year!

My name:

_____

The most awesome thing to happen in 2014:

_____

_____

The funniest thing to happen in 2014:

_____

_____

The bravest thing I did:

_____

_____

The thing I could have done better:

_____

_____

Top friends:

_____

_____

_____

My 3 ambitions for 2015 are:

_____

_____

_____

The best

My fav

The f

The

The

M

SPEED CONTROL

The faster you can get to your enemy, the better. They won't see you coming! Add up the numbers in each path to find the quickest route to the Kraangdroids.

a

b

c

d

2 seconds

1 seconds

5 seconds

1 seconds

2 seconds

3 seconds

3 seconds

1 seconds

3 seconds

2 seconds

2 seconds

3 seconds

2 seconds

2 seconds

1 seconds

1 seconds

3 seconds

2 seconds

THE FASTEST ROUTE IS:

Answers on page 65.

49

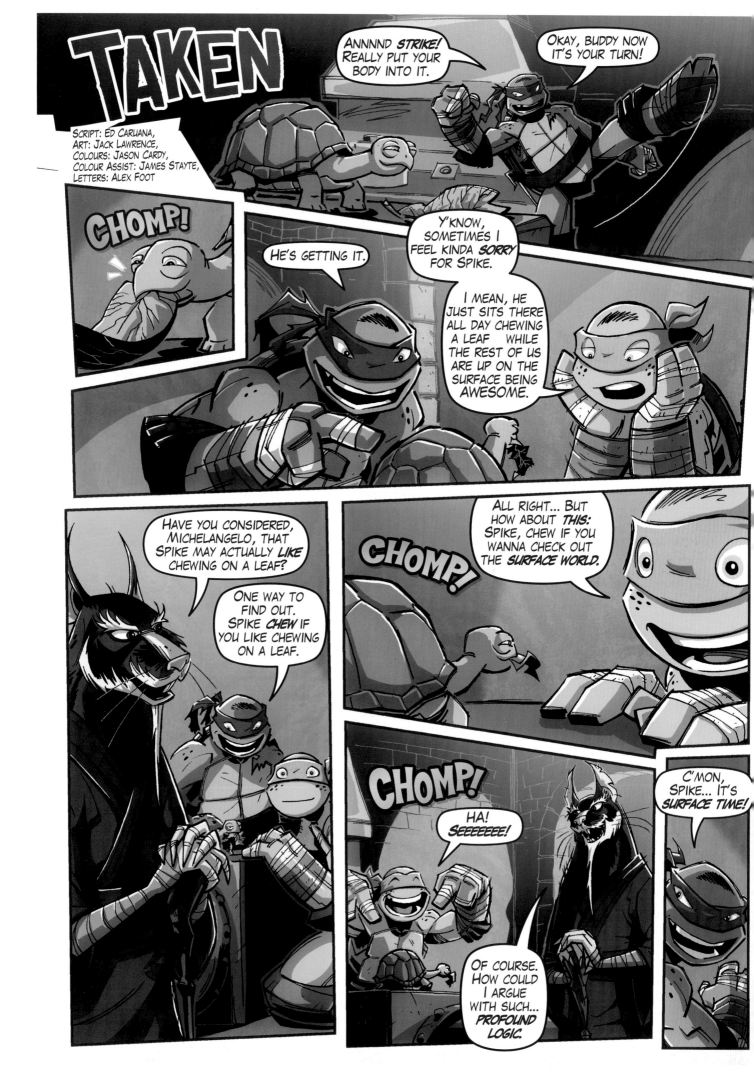

OOZE ATTACK

Can you work out who is who when they're covered in mutagen?

BOOM!

1

2

3

4

5

6

Write the correct number in each circle.

a

b

c

d

e

f

Answers on page 64.

EVIL CREATION

There are lots of bad mutants
in the city. Now it's your turn to
create another one! Think up the scariest mutant
you can and draw it in the space below. Remember to give it a name
and list its powers.

name: _____

special powers: _____

_____

RELEASE THE NINJA BOMBS!

START →

April is in trouble! She's been captured by Kraang Prime so he can steal her DNA. Casey Jones and Raphael need to get to the warehouse and fast.

The only problem is, Slash and Mutagen Man are chasing them!

FINISH

Find your way through the maze to April, making sure you pass through every smoke bomb on the way to throw Slash and Mutagen Man off the scent!

Answers on page 65.

GUIDE TO BEING AN AWESOME NINJA!

Ninjas aren't brawlers. They don't beat their enemies into submission. A ninja is something different. Read on to find out how ninjutsu training makes a ninja AWESOME!

OBSERVE

Watch the enemy. See how they tick. The more you understand your enemy, the better ninja you'll be.

Here's Leo watching the enemy.

did you know?

Splinter is an awesome teacher in ninjutsu. If only the Turtles would just pay attention!

DISGUISE

Use the shadows to confuse the bad guys. Trick your enemy.

Check Mikey out throwing a ninja smoke bomb to bamboozle the Kraang!

OPEN MIND

Open your mind to using different weapons and gadgets to your advantage.

Raph used a throwing star to put the Kraang van out of action!

Leo spends all his spare time training – and it really shows.

TRAIN

Train, train and train some more!

NATURE

Use wind, fire, water and light to help you in battle. Keep nature on your side.

Here are the Turtles using lightning to trap Snakeweed!

Check out Donnie with his six-foot bo!

WEAPON

Every ninja has a favourite weapon. Choose your weapon and get to know it better than anyone else in the world.

Did you know?

Ninjutsu began in Japan in the 6th century. It's over 1500 years old!

61

SMASH!

Mikey has been practising some dance moves and has smashed Splinter's favourite photo of the Turtles in training! Can you help him fix it before Splinter gets home? Find the broken pieces below in the big picture.

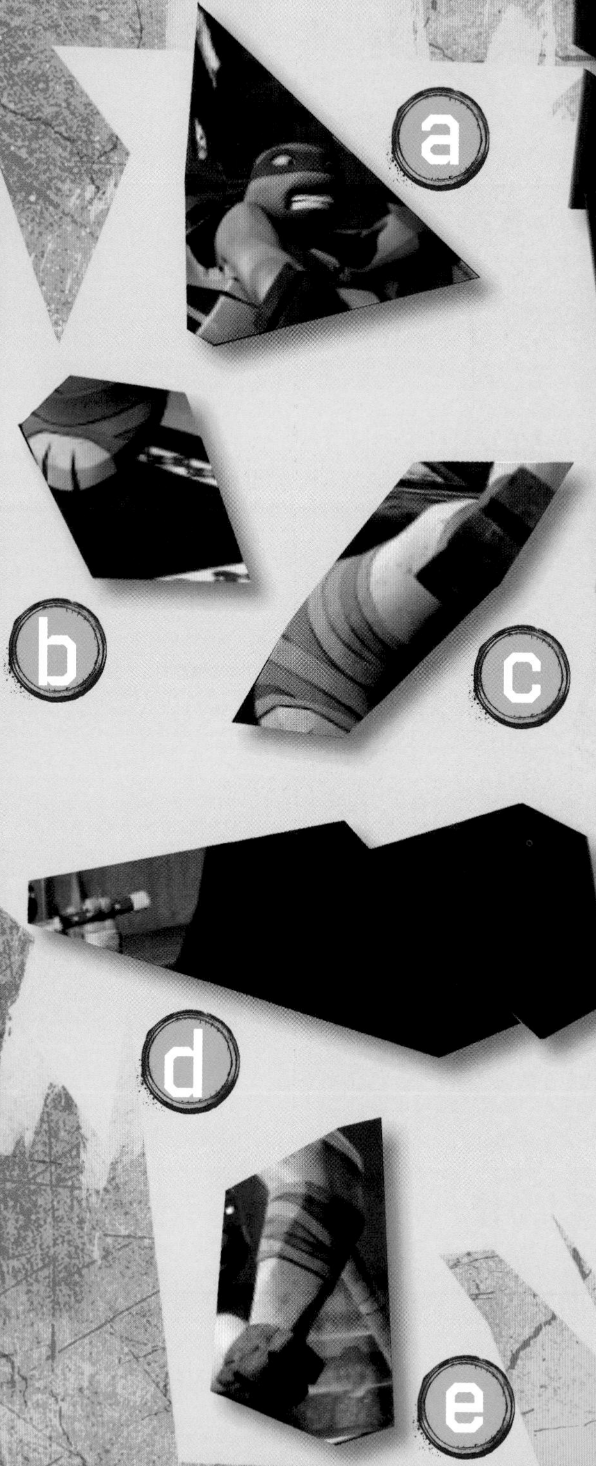

a

b

c

d

e

When you have finished, see if you can find
Spike the tortoise hiding in the picture!

Answers on page 65.

ANSWERS

P.9 concentrate!
C and J are the same

P.11 BOMB OUT!

P.15 RAPH ATTACKS!
1. Leo
2. Casey Jones
3. Shredder
4. Karai

P.25 hidden message
We will wait for the Turtles opposite Antonio's Pizza Restaurant. We know they will be there at 5 o'clock. They can't resist cheese pizza. The Turtles cannot escape the mighty Shredder any longer. Nobody must learn of this plot to assassinate the Turtles. It is a top-secret mission. Message over.

64

P.29 DIMENSION X

portal to earth!

P.30 MUTANT EXPLOSION

P.38 MEAN STREETS CHALLENGE

P.40 EVIL SEARCH!

Shredder's message:
Destroy Turtles

P.49 SPEED CONTROL

The fastest route is d.

P.56 OOZE ATTACK

1-e, 2-a, 3-b, 4-f, 5-d and 6-c.

P.62 SMASH!

P.58 RELEASE THE NINJA BOMBS!

SHELL YA LATER, DUDES!